Me
& My
Electric

Also by Elizabeth Laird

Forbidden Ground
Hiding Out
Jay
Kiss the Dust
Red Sky in the Morning

For younger readers

A Funny Sort of Dog
On the Run
Secret Friends

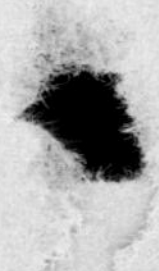

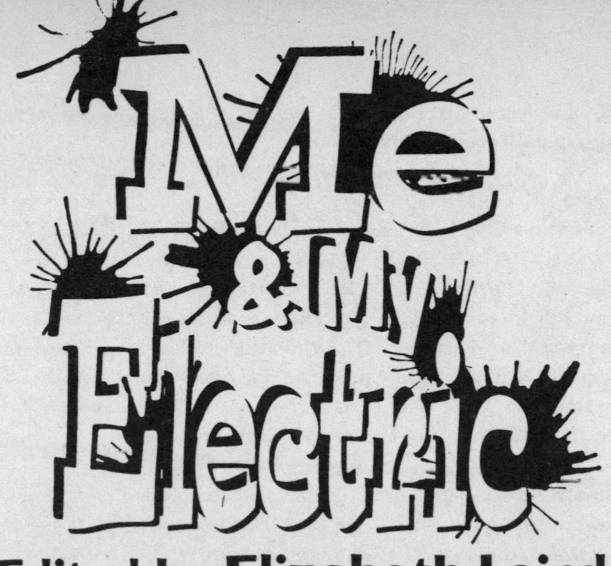

Edited by Elizabeth Laird

Illustrated by
Polly Dunbar

First published in Great Britain in 1998 by Mammoth
an imprint of Egmont Children's Books Limited
239 Kensington High Street, London W8 6SA

ISBN 0 7497 2922 8

10 9 8 7 6 5 4 3

A CIP catalogue record for this book
is available from the British Library

Typeset by Avon Dataset Ltd, Bidford on Avon, B50 4JH
Printed in Great Britain by Cox & Wyman Ltd, Reading, Berkshire

Contents

Foreword

Why are so many of the bad people in books disabled? There's Captain Hook with only one hand in *Peter Pan*, the evil witch in *Hansel and Gretel* leaning on her crutch, and Rumpelstiltskin, the 'dwarf'.

If they're not evil, disabled people in books are often seen as poor little victims, like Tiny Tim in *A Christmas Carol*, who 'bore a little crutch and had his limbs supported by an iron frame'.

In real life, of course, disabled people are just like everyone else. Some are fun, some are shy, some are friendly, some like heavy metal, some are mad about Beethoven, some sing, some don't, some like steak and chips, some are vegetarian, some wear miniskirts, some don't talk much, and some never stop.

'We don't want people to say how awful life is for us, or how wonderful we are,' a disabled person said to me, 'but how we are different and how we are the same.'

In this book, seven young people are telling it as it is for them. And seven writers have been their 'scribes', to help them with the difficult business of writing a proper story.

So now it's up to you. Read all about Sang and Roz and Ashveena and Rebecca and Lucy and Scott and Matthew so that you can get to know them too.

Elizabeth Laird
1998

Foreword

from Save the Children

Save the Children is a large charity, working in over fifty countries around the world, including the United Kingdom. We work with children with disabilities, and think it's time disabled children had the chance to tell their own stories. Too often adults tell us what children are thinking, or should be thinking. We're delighted that *Me and My Electric* is written *by* disabled children, not just about them.

We helped create an international law called the United Nations Convention on the Rights of the Child. It says that all children, including disabled children, have the right to be heard. If you'd like to find out more about our work, please call our Public Enquiry Unit on 0171 703 5400.

We hope you enjoy these stories and that they give you the chance to look at the world in new ways.

Tina Hyder, Development Officer, 1998

Freewheeling Champ

Davoren Hanna

(For Stephen Roche)

I listened to the roar
of victory in my ears.
Inch by painful inch
I rode with him –
plummeting downhill,
swerving, gliding,
rising with his wry
Dublin humour
rolling in my spokes.
Satin-ribbon roads
slipped under my wheels,
but undaunted came I
to vanquish all doubt
riding in triumph
on to the Champs Elysées.

Me and My Electric

Scott Thurlby with June Counsel

It *was* to be Mum's honeymoon, her second honeymoon, just Mum and Ian, and my dad was going to have Hayley and me. (Hayley's my sister. She's eleven and I'm twelve, and Dad has access.) But, at the last moment, Dad couldn't have us, so Mum said, 'Well, that's it then, isn't it? You will just have to come!'

Four go on Honeymoon! But Mum wasn't too happy. After all a honeymoon is supposed to be just the two of you, not the four of you, not two adults *and* two kids. But, as it turned out, it wasn't even the four of us, it was the six of us! A friend of Mum's, Trudi, said she and her boyfriend, Rodney, would come. They'd *love* a Spanish holiday and *they'd* look after Hayley and me.

Mum's known them years. Trudi's good to be with. She's tiny and bubbly and really, really pretty. Rodney generally acts the comedian. He ought to be on the stage, he's so funny. Anything that comes out of his mouth is funny, he doesn't have to try. He never stops mucking about. Once, when I was sitting in the garden under the bathroom window, he nipped in the house, got a jug, ran upstairs and poured a whole lot of cold water splash on to my head from the bathroom window!

Mum often says to Trudi, 'How on earth do you put up with him?'

Trudi always says, 'I don't know! I just don't know.'

But she goes on putting up with him.

Ian, my new stepdad, is tall, six foot one and muscly. He's a window fabricator, makes windows up in UPVC. He supports Leeds United while I support Man U. When the two clubs play each other it's horrible. We go round the pub to watch it on Sky, and sit there nudging each other and saying, 'You're losing! We're playing better than you!' The last time they played each other, Leeds beat Man U 3–1. Ian was really winding me up all the time and when the final whistle blew, he jumped up, banged on the table and shouted, 'Yes! *Yes*! YES!'

Six of us going was better. Mum said so, and she laughed and smiled and said what fun it would be. Hayley was thrilled, Trudi and Rodney were over the moon. Ian was pleased. And me – how did I feel? I'll tell you how I felt. Scared, *dead* scared. Terrified, in fact, but I didn't let on. I'd never been abroad before and, actually, Mum had never flown before.

The flight over was all right. There were five other wheelchairs so that was a comfort, not being the only one, though I was the only child. My wheelchair's electric, but I can switch it to manual if I want to. It takes to bits in seconds – well, Mum and Ian can take it to bits in seconds, when you want to stow it somewhere. It's like a second body to me. I know all the controls. I can weave in and out of our rooms; I can reverse. I can go out to the shops on my own, and to my favourite pub with Ian and Mum.

We flew from Stansted Airport. When we, the 'wheelchairs', were got out of our wheelchairs, we were put, one by one, into a carrying chair and carried up the steps and into the plane and then manoeuvred into our seats. The carrying chair had a safety belt and footrests. I can stand and walk a *bit*, if Mum or Ian get behind me and put their forearms under my shoulders to give me support and steady me. So I got aboard all right, and my electric was whisked away and stowed somewhere in the plane.

But, at Palma Airport in Majorca, it was *terrifying*!

A mob of Spaniards in light blue shirts, no ties, and dark blue trousers, rushed at me and started getting me out of my seat. Only one spoke English. He kept saying, 'Stay still, stay still, stay *still*!' But I couldn't stay still, I was shaking so. I couldn't stop shaking. All their movements were so quick. They were heaving and hauling me about as though I were a parcel they had to get to the post, and the post was just about to go. I kept saying, 'Hey, what's the hurry? Slow down, slow *down*. What's the rush? Do you have to catch a bus or what?'

The one that spoke a bit of English waved at Mum to go with the other passengers who were leaving the plane, but when I saw the carrying chair they were going to put me into, I said, 'I'm not going in that carrying chair unless Mum's with me!' because it had no safety belt and no footrests. It was just a metal chair with a canvas back and a canvas seat. Mum said to the chap, 'No, I'm staying with him!' Meaning me, and she stayed.

They finally got me in the carrying chair and carried me out on to the top step – and I really panicked. It was so far from the ground, so far! I thought, oh, I'm going to fall, I'm going to fall off, and I shan't bounce neither, because I'm a heavy-built chap.

I didn't fall. They carried me down safely and there was my electric waiting for me, and was I glad to be back in it, and in control. I *know* those

Spaniards had to be quick, because planes have to keep to schedules, but if someone could have explained to me what was going to happen, what they were doing, and if they'd got a safer-looking carrying chair, I wouldn't have been so scared.

As soon as I was on the ground I thought, phew! Thank God that's over. Thank God I don't have to do that again for another week, because all the time it was happening, I was thinking, this is the *worst* bit of my holiday.

A weird sort of bus with a wide door and a tail-lift was waiting for the wheelchairs, and the Spaniards started putting me on the tail-lift, and again they waved at Mum to go with the other passengers on the ordinary bus, but I shouted, 'She's coming with me. I ain't being left alone with a lot of strangers.'

And Mum said, 'I'm not leaving Scott.' And she whipped in after me as the doors shut.

When we got outside the airport to the bus that would take us to the hotel, we saw that it was an ordinary bus with very steep steps, and there wasn't any special help. Mum and Ian got me out of the electric. Rodney got up on the steps and turned to face me. Ian went behind me and put his forearms under my shoulders and walked me a pace or two to the foot of the steps. Rodney leaned down and took hold of my arms. Two holidaymakers came to help Ian and the three of them pushed and shoved me from behind, and Rodney pulled and pulled on my arms till, bit by bit, they got me into the bus. It didn't half hurt. My arms felt as though they'd been pulled out of their sockets, but I didn't say anything. Of course, when we got to the hotel, there was all the business of getting me *down* the steps, but at least my arms weren't being pulled.

At last we *were* there and I was back in my electric. I saw there was a ramp up to the hotel and I thought, this bit *I'm* doing, because I like driving myself.

'Right, let's go!' I said to Mum and off we started, but the ramp was too steep, and too narrow. I was frightened I'd wobble over or slide back, and Mum had to grab hold. So, in the end, Mum pushed and I steered and we got up to the doors, which were wide, and – we were in!

Our bedrooms were on the third floor and there was only room in the lift for the electric and one other person, so usually Mum went up with me, and the others walked.

The bedrooms had balconies, but our bedroom was so full of furniture with Mum and Ian's double bed and Hayley and my bunk beds and other stuff, that I couldn't drive my electric near the balcony. So I used to go into Trudi and Rodney's room and drive up to their balcony, and sit there by the open balcony door looking out. I never drove *on* to the balcony, I was scared to, but I loved sitting just where it began, and looking at the sea. That sea. I couldn't believe it. It was so blue, so clear, such a bright, clear blue, as though nothing dirty had ever been in it. A clean, clean, *clean* blue.

We parked my electric in our bathroom. The bathroom was as crowded as our bedroom! But I had fun in that bathroom. I could lie down and have a bubble bath and a shower at the same time. I can't do that at home. I can have a bubble bath, but not a shower, because the shower's upstairs. Of course, I was careful always to keep my mouth shut. I knew you mustn't swallow Spanish water. Mum kept drinking the water, ice cubes, squash, and it made her ill.

I loved the Spanish food, especially paella and rice. There was a sauce you squeezed out of a bottle, not one I've ever seen in England. I squeezed it over rice and paella and salads and just about everything, and it was wonderful. Mum and Hayley and Ian and Trudi didn't like Spanish food. Mum kept eating salads and getting tummy upsets.

The beaches were very rocky and pebbly. You could only get down to them by long flights of concrete steps, so we didn't bother. We went to the hotel swimming pool instead. We'd go straight there after breakfast and stay till mid-afternoon. Mum would get the electric to the pool side. Then Ian would put his forearms under my shoulders and walk me to the steps or lower me on to the edge. Mum would have slipped into the water, and she'd be there to get me. I wore armbands, but I'm fine in water! As soon as I'm in it, I'm just like other kids. I can even walk! I'm a good swimmer. I skinny-dipped at school once – it was great. I've done a marathon for British Telecom. I swam sixteen widths and I was only meant to do fifteen, and we only had thirty minutes to do it in.

There were all sorts of children there: German, Dutch, Swedish, Spanish, of course, and English. There was a boy from Sunderland. We mucked about and had fun and splashed each other, and I was one of them, no different.

One day, a mum got into the pool with a little boy of about four or five, and he was screaming and screaming.

I went to her and said, 'What's the matter with him?'

She said, 'He's scared.'

So I said to him, 'What have you got to be scared of? You have a bath at home, don't you?'

He sobbed, 'Y-yes.'

I said, 'Well, that's water, and this is only

water. You don't have to be scared of this. It's just a big bath.'

And I stayed by him, and *didn't* splash him, and after a while he stopped being scared and began to like it.

It wasn't just kids who had fun in the pool, or just kids who mucked about. Rodney pushed Trudi in! He did it on the spur of the moment. She was fully clothed, standing on the edge of the pool talking, and the next moment, SPLASH!

she was in, swimming about, trying to grab her handbag and things. You had to laugh. Rodney was creasing himself. We were all laughing. Well, not Trudi. Water's wonderful. It makes you – free.

Trudi spluttered, 'Bridget's camera's in my handbag, you idiot!'

Rodney leaned forward and took the handbag from her, so she could climb out. Mum's camera wasn't in it when she looked. Mum had taken it out. Her camera's got a wriststrap on it, so she can take it with her and still have her hands free.

Rodney's fun. He never has a down side. He was always fun.

He and Trudi had told Mum they'd look after Hayley and me for two hours each day, so she and Ian could go for a walk. But the holiday turned out such fun that mostly we were all together doing things, and laughing and eating.

I don't think Mum and Ian minded their honeymoon turning into a holiday for all of us. Once, when I was in the pool, I looked across the water and saw them lying on a bed at the poolside, kissing and cuddling. So I reckon as a honeymoon the holiday was all right, too.

Rodney's very skilled; he doesn't always clown. He's a plasterer, works for himself. Mum's last birthday, he and Ian made a surprise birthday cake for her. They made two sponges and then stuck them together with jam and cream. They put *three* eggs into each sponge! Mum couldn't get over that. 'Imagine,' she kept saying, '*six* eggs in one cake.' They did icing too, and they wrote on it in icing without *one* mistake. Mum says nearly always when you're doing icing writing you make a mistake and have to nick a bit out and do it again, but Rodney and Ian did it right first time.

Our hotel was on the outskirts of a little town called Cala de Mallorca. It had a little tractor sort of train, which pulled carriages, to take guests into Cala to see the shops and clubs. The train had different stops, including one at the beach and one where all the shops were.

One day we all got on this little train and went to Cala to see the shops. We spent the morning there and walked round all of them. When we'd had enough we went back to the train and Ian put me on it. Hayley, Trudi and Rodney got on, and Mum and Ian. Then me and Hayley decided we wanted a burger. So Mum got off and went to Burger King and ordered two burger and chips. The service was so slow, and the train was about to go, so we called to her to come and get on it quick. But she said, 'Well, I've paid for them, so I must wait!'

Ian jumped off and went to wait with her, and the train went! Hayley cried out, 'Where's Mum? Where's Ian?'

Me and Rodney started to crack up, but Hayley was really agitated and began to cry. She thought she'd never see Mum or Ian again.

It got funnier still when we got back to the hotel. Mum and Ian were there! They'd taken a taxi and got back before us. When we said, 'Where's our burgers then?' they said, 'We've eaten them. We didn't know how long the taxi would take!'

We did laugh. Next morning, when we were going on the little train again, I told Mum I'd like a replay, I'd enjoyed yesterday so much. Hayley didn't, though.

Sometimes we'd walk down to a little club and sit drinking. I'd have a coke, not that the coke was very nice, because it wasn't, or I'd have an orange or a lime. One evening, when it was getting really late, Ian decided it was time to go, and he said, 'We'll have a taxi.' He didn't want to walk any more, because he and Mum and Hayley had been walking all day.

So we all went out and he hailed a taxi. At least, he thought it was a taxi, it had a flashing sign. But it wasn't! It was a police car full of policemen, bare-headed, and with guns, and two of them were nursing a big, black box.

The chief policeman said, 'There are no taxis after nine pm.'

Ian pointed to us and said, 'Wife, daughter, son want a lift, please.'

The policeman was *so* nice. He chucked the other policemen out. He chucked the big, black box out. He helped Mum and Ian dismantle the electric and put it in the boot. Then he drove us back to the hotel. He got the electric out again and helped Mum put it together, and helped me into it. He was so helpful. I don't know what the other policemen did. Whether they just hung about with their big, black box, or whether they went into the club and had a drink.

When the last day came and we were back at Palma Airport, I saw this lorry in the distance. It started driving towards me, really towards me, and I'm thinking, why's it coming towards *me*, why's it stopping by *me*? Then the driver and another man got out, opened the doors, and came up to me.

'On you go!' they said, and this time, they never said to Mum, 'Off *you* go, too!'

So Mum and Ian got in with me, and the other wheelchairs, and when the lorry got to the plane – the inside of the lorry went up! We were still inside it, we hadn't moved, and we went up! Up to the plane doorway! I drove to my seat, which was near the entrance, and a steward and Ian put me in my seat and took my electric away. It was as simple as that. Wish we'd had that lorry there when we arrived. Hayley and Trudi and Rodney, of course, came in the ordinary bus with the other guests.

All the way home I was bubbling. It had been such a marvellous holiday, such fun. Mucking about in the pool with the other kids, splashing and swimming. And I'd helped that little boy! The sea. That clean, clean sea, so blue, so beautiful. I thought, I'm going to travel and travel and *travel.*

I said to Mum, 'America next time!'

Then I noticed her nails. Usually she keeps them long and painted but they were all bitten down to the quick.

'Mum, your nails!'

She said, 'I've been chewing them all week. I was so frightened. Every day there was a new hazard, I was just waiting for an accident to happen, for you to be injured.'

Well! *Both* of us so scared. Both of us terrified. All that fear inside us and neither telling. We had to laugh. I said again, 'America next, Mum. I'm travelling!'

We will too, me and my electric.

I Like Being Horrible

Rebecca Atkinson with Joyce Dunbar

My life is so horrible nowadays. Everything about my life is horrible. This house is horrible. The furniture is horrible. This family I've been forced to live with is horrible. Even my dad is horrible. But the most horrible thing of all is me. Horrible! Horrible! Horrible!

I'm learning to like being horrible.

I sit here, on my bed in my so-called room – though I call it a broom cupboard. My hair is greasy and needs washing. My chin is covered in spots. I look just the way I feel – horrible.

We've just had another row! About the cats again. We'd just sat down to supper – all six of us, when Jessica – one of my horrible stepsisters, said it was my turn to clean up the cat sick.

'Why should it be my turn?' I said. 'It's your cat that's been sick, not mine!'

'How do you know it's mine?'

'Because my cat is never sick!'

'Neither was mine, till you came to live here!'

'I didn't ask to live here!'

Then Dad joins in. He quietly puts down his knife and fork and heaves a big sigh.

'Can't you pack it in, you two? We're trying to have a meal.'

Then Jessica's mum, my horrible stepmother, joins in.

'We don't know whose cat has been sick, but it's only fair to take it in turns, for heaven's sake. Holly, you do it after supper.'

'I can't!' I wailed. 'Cleaning up cat sick makes me sick! And, anyway, I didn't want to come here and live with you lot. I liked it where I was. I liked being with my dad. We didn't need you. We don't want you!'

And then I stormed off to my broom cupboard, which is where I am now. I've got Pushkin with me. He's got lovely soft white paws and black and ginger splodges. Not like their cat. A dumpy thing called Tinkerbell. Tinkerbell! I ask you! Stinkerbell more like. And it was definitely Stinkerbell sick.

*

I'd better explain.

Four years ago, everything was all right. I lived with my mum and dad and my older sister Vicky.

Vicky's not horrible, Vicky's great. But she left home ages ago and is a student at art school. At the moment, she's in Mexico, making a video. Whoever would have thought it? I can't wait to go off on my own.

Vicky and I had always wanted to travel. Being deaf is no excuse. Vicky's deafer than me now – suddenly lost the rest of her hearing and doesn't even wear hearing-aids. I have to wear one. I manage. I manage just fine.

But three and a half years ago, Vicky started bumping into things. She wanted the light on all the time, even in broad daylight. Mum took her for a sight test.

She was told she had Usher's syndrome.

They said this Usher's syndrome runs in families and I should be tested as well.

And guess what, folks? I've got it too!

Usher! I wish I'd never heard that word.

I was so angry. I'm still angry. Why Vicky?

Why me? It's not fair! And there isn't even anyone to blame.

When Vicky and I were first told, we were so numb that we couldn't even talk to each other about it. We didn't really know what it meant. We thought we were going to go blind as well as deaf. We were given all these pamphlets to read, which made me even more furious – as if they were rubbing our noses in it. But then Mum did manage to get it through to me that my hearing wouldn't necessarily get worse, and that we wouldn't go completely blind. We'd be able to see straight ahead, but not all around. And we wouldn't be able to see at all in the dark. Tunnel vision they call it. Vicky's got it already. She says it's like looking at everything through a loo roll.

We were asked if we wanted to go away to this special grammar school. Vicky chose to go. But not me. I like my school. And my mates.

I didn't cry much, except when Vicky left home. She cried too. I remember looking at her red face and puffy eyes and pouty mouth.

'You look pathetic!' I said.

'So do you,' she said.

'At least we can still see how we look,' I joked.

'Let's see who can look the most pathetic,' she said.

And we sat in front of the mirror, making pathetic faces. Mine was really good. I stuck my hair behind my ears to look sad, then turned my lips in to show my teeth and rolled my eyes. I looked really goofy. Vicky did the same. We sat there, making faces and giggling, for ages.

It felt good. We didn't do much giggling in those days. Then we walked in on Mum and Dad wearing our pathetic faces. They didn't laugh. They just stared.

They seemed to be in a permanent state of shock. They'd never heard of this Usher thing and couldn't bear to think that their two precious daughters had it. They mooched around, pale as ashes, white as ghosts.

'Cheer up. It's us who've got the problem,' I said.

Mum joined a support group for other parents whose children had Usher's. Dad just buried himself in his work so that we hardly saw him.

Then, to cut a long story short, Mum did something to cheer herself up. She fell in love with one of the blokes in the support group. She said she was going to start a national support network with him.

What did Dad do?

He cracked up. Just what we needed.

We soon forgot our Usher's syndrome, I can tell you.

I remember one afternoon when Vicky was away at school and Mum had gone too. It was one of those grey, nothing-doing sort of days, as if it wants to rain but can't. I walked into the kitchen and found Dad all crumpled up in a heap, crying.

It was then that I found out I was horrible.

I didn't put my arm round him or make him a cup of tea or anything like that. I hated him. I didn't want this pathetic scrunched creature for a dad. I wanted my own dad, who liked to have a laugh and had always been so kind. I just wanted to shake him. But I didn't. Instead, I walked out of the kitchen and left him there.

So what happened next? Mum moved off to live with her boyfriend. She asked me to go too – but what about my school? What about my friends? I decided to stay with Dad.

Dad and I were on our own for two years. At first I hated it. But looking back, I can see it was all right. Mum used to be dead fussy about what we ate and how we ate it – but not Dad. He stocked up with TV dinners and pizzas and we ate what we liked when we liked.

And living with Dad was just so easy. He knows how to talk to me. He never shouts, just makes sure I can see him. He puts teletext on TV when I'm watching and he always puts the light on even before he thinks I need it.

My dad's a counsellor. He counsels people in trouble – but he wasn't much good at counselling himself. He met this woman – my stepmother – on one of his counselling courses, and soon he was talking about moving in with her.

He didn't ask me what I wanted. Just said it

would be much better in the long run for us to be part of a large family, a real family, and we'd all learn to get on together in the end, and so forth.

Moving in was a nightmare. First, they had to find a bigger house, big enough for all of us. We found one in the end, so expensive that my dad will need to live to be 120 to pay for it! I insisted on my own room and was awarded the broom cupboard.

And the furniture! None of it matched. Ours is lovely old stuff that Mum picked up in junk shops. Theirs is all shiny and modern. And there was so much of it that Dad had to have a shed built to put the spare stuff in. Some days I think the house will be sick, throw up all the furniture through the doors and windows. Think of it. Spewing furniture all over the garden. I'd like that.

And mealtimes! We all have to sit round the table at set times and make conversation. There's Martin, my horrible stepbrother, who picks his nose in between picking at the food if my dad's cooked it. He'll never eat my dad's food. I have to eat his mum's! And they all talk together so that I'm left out. And then when they do think of saying something to me, they shout at me, as if I'm some kind of dumbo.

My stepmother's learning sign language. She tries to teach me. No way. I'll learn it when the rest of the world does. She'll have to talk sign language to herself.

So here we are. Two stepsisters, a stepbrother, and two cats who hate each other just as much as we all do. What would I do if my dad died? I couldn't live here.

I will not clean up the cat sick.

I will not help with the chores. (That's another sore point. We used to have enough money and a cleaning lady. Now there's hardly any money and we have a rota for chores. I ask you. It's like an army camp sometimes.)

I will not wash my hair.

I will not put TCP on my spots.

I like being horrible.

*

Thank goodness for school. Thank goodness for my mates. We started a rolling love letter in the maths lesson. Everyone adding a bit and then folding it over. Afterwards, we went into the art room and read it out. Some people have filthy minds! I think it's Tim. He likes to shock everyone just because his dad's a vicar.

Anyway, we were all there, Tim and his crowd and a few of us girls. We got into a mood where everything we said was hilarious, even if it wasn't.

I put on my aren't-I-pathetic? face.

I've got it down to a fine art now. I can flare my nostrils really wide and roll my eyes so that only the whites show.

'Aw! Give us a kiss,' I squeak. 'Please will you get off with me?'

They all laugh. Hysterics.

'All my friends have got boyfriends,' I wheedle. 'I want one too. But I'm ugly. Do you think I'm ugly? Will you be my boyfriend?'

By now, we're all laughing so much that I have to stop.

Jake – that's my boyfriend – he's the worst of

the lot. He says that's why he likes me so much. My sense of humour. (Sometimes I think he likes me too much – but I'll invent a code for those bits.) Ah. But he doesn't know how horrible I am. Horrible is strictly for home.

Like yesterday evening. The phone went four times, for me. I can't hear the phone if I'm in my room so one of my step-so-and-sos has to come and get me.

I was going back to my room when I heard Jessica moaning at her mum. I tried to listen but couldn't hear what they were saying.

Then I caught sight of them in the kitchen mirror and could *see* what they were saying. I can lip-read you see. It has its uses.

'Why is the phone always for her? Why is it never for me?' Jessica moaned.

Her mum just shook her head.

'And she leaves it on so loud. When I pick it up, it nearly blows my head off.'

'You can easily turn it down.'

'And why can she go on sleepovers and not me?' I saw Jessica say.

'Because she gets invited, I expect,' said her mum. 'Perhaps if you were a bit nicer to each other she'd invite you too.'

'I am nice to her. Anyway, I think she makes it all up – this Usher's syndrome thing. She hears when she wants to all right. And she sees what she wants to see.'

'Don't be so unkind. It's true that she manages very well. It's true that she doesn't complain. She shouldn't be blamed for that. And if the phone keeps ringing for her, that's because she's popular. You can't begrudge her that.'

'I don't. And anyway, their cat's got fleas.'

This was too much for me. I barged in.

'Whose cat's got fleas?' I asked.

That shook her, I can tell you. She thinks she can say what she likes about me and I won't hear.

'If it has, it caught them off you!'

I wish they all had Usher's syndrome, just for one day, so that they would know what it was like.

Well, you'll never guess what happened tonight

at supper-time. We were on the subject of cat sick again when Martin turned quite green and stopped picking his nose. Then he threw up. All over the table! Ughhh!

I can't believe I wrote all that. Only two weeks ago and everything's changed. Martin was more than sick. He had a headache and a high temperature and then started saying the light hurt his eyes. Then he got a purple rash. He was rushed off to hospital. They said he'd got something awful – meningitis. It can kill you! It can make you deaf and blind.

We all sat round, unable to believe what was happening.

When Tinkerbell brought a half-chewed-up mouse in, I was the one who moved it. And I saw Julie stroking Pushkin. 'Let him be all right. Let him be all right!' she was whispering.

And I wanted him to be all right too.

Suddenly, all those other things seemed unimportant. My broom cupboard. Greasy hair. Spots. The furniture that didn't match. And it didn't matter who cooked, because none of us wanted to eat. There were two days when we thought Martin might die! But he's out of the woods now.

It was all so dramatic. All the people Martin had been in touch with had to be traced in case they were infected too and we all had to have swabs taken and stuff like that.

And I forgot about being horrible.

I began to think how nice it could be, all of us together. My stepmother's quite nice really. She doesn't mind if I borrow her tights. And she helps me go over the French I haven't managed to hear. And Jessica isn't so bad. I was dyeing my hair one night – a colour called Shangrila – but couldn't see to do the back very well. Jessica walks in.

'Do you want any help?' she offered.

'All right.'

'It's all my fault,' she said, squeezing the stuff down my neck.

'What's your fault?' I asked.

'About Martin. It's my fault because I was so

rotten to you. Complaining about the TV being too loud and the telephone and that.'

'Don't worry,' I said. 'I'm not all that nice to you – or your mum.'

'Martin could go deaf,' she said, 'and blind.'

'He won't,' I said. 'It would be too much for one family.'

Jessica stopped abruptly, as if I'd said something peculiar.

'One family?' she asked. 'Is that what we are?'

'I suppose so,' I shrugged.

She stared at me for a while. I must have looked a sight, with my hair all wet and squidgy and Shangrila streaks running down my face. Then she said, very hesitantly, 'But what is it like, Holly? Really. What is it like to feel that you're going to be . . . you know . . . not being able to hear and that?'

'I don't know,' I said. 'It's just me – the way I am. I've never been able to hear properly so I've got nothing to compare it with.'

'But don't you *mind*?'

'Well, I mind when I'm on a sleepover and I

can't hear what the others are saying to each other in the dark . . . but at least I get some sleep. And I mind missing the jokes – and having to laugh just the same.'

(I didn't tell her about the other things I mind. Like having to ask someone for an arm to lean on in the dark – as if I were an old lady – and for the lights to be turned up when everyone wants them dim.)

'But you're always making jokes,' said Jessica. 'How do you keep so cheerful? How come you've got so many friends? I don't even get invited to sleepovers.' Then she started to cry.

I made my pathetic face for her. 'Oooh. Nobody loves me,' I said. 'I'm ugly. I've got spots. Do you think I'm ugly? Awww. Give us a kiss.'

And we both laughed, just like Vicky and I used to do. And I told her about Jake, and she said how gorgeous he was and she wanted to know if she could come out with us too and meet his brother.

Then I rinsed my hair and Jessica dried it for me and said she was going to dye her hair too.

'Shangrila!' she hooted, looking at the packet. 'I think I'll dye mine Tipperary!'

I haven't filled in my diary for ages. It's funny how I only want to write in it when I'm miserable, and I haven't been miserable for ages. I wonder why I never write the good things down? Because I'm too busy doing them I suppose. All the happy days are empty pages. Martin got better – and stopped picking at his nose and his food. Vicky came home – full of her travels. She showed us the video she had made. If Vicky can do all these things, so can I.

And we're getting on much better as a family. As soon as Vicky came back, I didn't feel so outnumbered. I stopped feeling like a visitor in my own home. And Mum has been too, with her bloke. Her support network is going well. She's getting a bookshop going and she's lobbying the government for all sorts of changes in opportunities for disabled people. And she does TV interviews and stuff like that. My mum! She's become quite a celebrity.

We still have our rows of course, like most big, happy families, only sometimes it's Jessica and me ganging up on her mum and my dad, telling them what a lousy mess they've made of things. And Dad just grins, to show how happy he is with the mess. But at least he's my dad again.

And I'm still horrible – but only sometimes – with the people who won't walk away.

Heavy Metal Man

Sang Bradby with Rachel Anderson

Where do I come from?

I don't know if that's true. But when I was small, I lost my birth certificate and I used to live in Vietnam in the children home and I was a young, little boy and I learn to walk about six or five. I seen the photo when I was young, and learning to walk, and playing bricks in Vietnam in Children's Home.

Vietnam is like a hot country and is a very small kind of city and the capital city is called Saigon and it's not called Saigon any more. It's called Ho Chi Minh. And it's changed a lot. And they didn't like the government because the government been mean to them.

I came to Britain by British aeroplane. And in a big jumbo all of us in a very neat line, by one by one. And they have a name-tag on them so they know the name of the person who it is. Everybody should have it. Because if you don't and you go or come Vietnam, can't go to the other country because you haven't got your name on it. Because you be lost.

I don't know if this is true. Maybe this wrong. But there was this boy, and his name is Sang, Nguyen Thanh Sang. This boy is born and his name is Sang. I may be wrong. And then I went to a Children's Home in England. I went with the other people when I was young. With other children who from Vietnam.

I can remember their names. It's very difficult if you don't understand their names. I explain their names because they're from Vietnam. Well, there was Mai. She is a small girl, the laughing one. Binh, who disabled so she can't talk properly and in a wheelchair and wear glasses and she can't feed herself. She can, except it's very difficult. And Ha. Ha can't walk. He can play with the Rubik cube. That is a plastic game with coloured squares. He's very clever. And Le, except can't walk except if two staff have to carry her or drag her sometimes. But it's very heavy to carry her. And Quoc is another one. He used to bite his arm and he used to have a massive big plaster to stop him biting his arm and he doesn't have it any more because he's stopped doing it. I think he learned because the staff trained him not to do it. Teach him to stop doing it now.

Kim-Yen. She screams a lot, or a little bit. But she learned to feed herself and sometimes the staff help her in case Kim-Yen make a mistake. I think she is younger than me. I don't know. You see, she's very difficult understanding. Some people don't understand what she's saying.

What is being adopted about?

When I was nine years old, I got new parents. Some people want to know what 'adopted' means. Like you just give someone a leaflet about adopting and say, 'Here you are, here's a leaflet.'

Well, I didn't like to talk to strangers about it when I was young. No way. But now it's OK to talk about it. I think so, because if they don't know about this, they need to know.

I was adopted by the Bradby family. I got two brothers, called Donald and one's called Lawrence. And the big sister is called Hannah and I was very nervous and I were very frightened and I don't know what it feel, well, how work, well, how a family.

They asked me, 'Would you like a parents?'

I had a social worker. She told me, 'I got a nice family called the Bradby.'

I thought that was very interesting but I don't know what I'm going to do. They didn't force me. They ask you, like, 'Would you like to meet some family? Would you like to see them?'

They don't force you because that don't make sense, no sense at all.

They lived in Canterbury in Kent. It was a small house called King Street and a very small town. They have a nice cathedral, like a big church. For the people praying and singing, interesting for the people who want to look around. I went to a school called Orchard School.

There's more things to do with parents and in a family. When I was about twelve, I was in a Christmas play, the three wise men. I was the gold. They did the play twice, once in school, then in the cathedral. It was very cold. I got cold feet. I wear costume, sort of funny hat and funny clothes. I carried the gold. It was just pretend gold. I had to say, 'Here is the gold.' As a present to Mary for Jesus.

Then I went to another school. It was OK the first time I went to have a look, but later I didn't like the dinner much. It was revolting cold potato and cold custard, not very nice at all. The gravy was just too lumpy. It was really disgusting. That was a boarding college. I stay there two years.

What do I like eating?

The best meal I like is a vegetable curry. I like to make it myself with curry powder. You can put anything you like: courgettes, chopped tomatoes, tinned tomatoes, sweetcorn, onions, peppers, mushrooms, maybe egg.

Boil the egg and peel the egg-shell and shove it in the curry with the vegetables round and the curry powder. And rice. Only people who like hot kind of food like it. Some people like very hot food. Some like it medium. I like it very hot because it's a really nice flavour. Chilli con carne, that'd be the same thing. It's just chilli powder and not putting in curry powder, but American red beans, out of a tin. It's very hot if you put loads of chilli powder in.

If you eat a hot thing, you should have a cold drink, like water or milk. You need something to cool you down because you could burn your mouth. It's not good for your mouth and it's not very good for your brain.

I would like to drink Coca-cola, except it's not

really good for you. If I have a hot curry, maybe I have ice-cream, or a sundae ice-cream made with a thing you can put on top.

I don't like liver. It tastes like rubber. I don't like the flavour or the taste of it.

What do I like doing?

There's Life Skills, and doing tests. Youth Training is like a training course. I want to learn skill. You can do mechanic and interviewing and plumbing and decorating. I want to do catering if I can: doing cooking, prepare food, and make it nice and just enjoy it and eating it. I like to work in hotel or restaurant, not a canteen.

My hobby is going out town, looking round the shops, looking round Our Price, the record shop, to see if I've got enough money to buy another tape. Sometimes I don't get enough time to buy it and it's so expensive. And sometimes I'm busy cleaning my new shoes, or listening to music.

The music I like – if you don't like it you don't

have to agree – is: I like Heavy Metal, hard metal.

It's very difficult to get the right person to share the right music. My favourite metal is Iron Maiden and if you don't know what Iron Maiden is, Iron Maiden is a British band and they come from Sheffield. There are so many names of

records: 'The Beast', 'The Killer'. They're all so difficult to say and to understand. One they made is 'Dying for Me', something about dying. I've got the T-shirt. It's really hard rock, it's very rock. You can't understand what they're going on about. Drums, electric guitar, microphone, and I think that's it.

I like going to the funfair. I like going out to enjoy myself. I like going with other people because then you have more fun. I like going with friends and family, with my sister. I just pop and see her and then we go out together. We go to the river, we talk to each other and look at the people.

About some sad things

I've got two brothers. I try to get on with them. Sometimes I have a row with them. That's what brothers and sisters do. You can't do anything about it. Except we forget it later. And I got relations: Granny, Grandpa, some cousins, all nice relations, and we got a cat called Cherry.

She hunts animals. She kills it, then just leaves it.

A long time ago, I've seen in the paper about loads of people trying to get out of Vietnam to Hong Kong and the government not doing very well, the government being silly. And the people being captured by the pirates, and some people are sunk.

A long time ago, I had a friend. She used to come see me. We used to go down by the river to a nice park and we feed the ducks. That's all. I was seeing her every few weeks, a very nice friend, really nice to me. She died. She had illness and she couldn't look after me at all. She couldn't adopt me at all.

When we die we might see her. I don't know, because you don't know what it's like when you go heaven.

My grandpa died. He was eighty-five. He died of illness. He didn't remember things. He just remembered my name.

An important day

One day, I had to sign a promise. I had to swear at a piece of paper. I had to promise I be a British, that kind of thing. Or an English. I been asked some words were so difficult. I had to swear to Queen Elizabeth the Second. And William. That's what it said on the paper. I think that's her son. Then someone had to sign it, a doctor or a solicitor or a law person. It took a long time. And afterwards we went off to the cathedral, it's quite big, tall, and there's a statue and a nice ceiling with pictures. If you look at the pictures properly, then you can tell the story quite well.

One of the pictures is Jesus Christ being born, nice and warm, sheep in the stable. At Christmas we hang up our stocking by the fire and I think the real Father Christmas comes, and next day you find, ooh, a stocking. We went to see Mum and Dad in bed, open presents. Donald sort of wakes me up and says, 'Come on, Sang. Wake up. Get your stocking.' Donald drags me out of bed.

If you've got nice parents and all your friends are nice to you, you've got to be nice to them sometimes. It's not nice to your parents if you're not. So the son or the daughter should help and be nice to them.

What's going to happen when I'm older?

I think it's nice to meet other people and do what you want. So I will move one day. When I done Youth Training, when I'm old enough. I like to find a flat with nice neighbours. I like to do what I want, like, when you want to have a shower, you don't share the bathroom. It's nice for people to get married. If you want to get married you should get the right person, you really like. If she's nice to you and you really get on well, I think you can get married. But if you get the wrong person, it's a waste of time. It wastes your life. It's really hard work for you. That's not making sense, that's not good. It's very silly.

Some more about adoption

If you really want a family, you need to find a really good social worker who can help you find one. And you need to meet the family, in the children's home, or somewhere. And then stay one weekend. Then stay a summer holiday. Then the parents should have a talk with the social worker, and the person who wants to be adopted.

It's quite difficult being adopted. I've got different skin and colour and I got different hair. Some of them, in the children's home, were adopted and others not. They stay in the children's home for ever. It's very sad. It would be nice to have my real parents. I wish I could go back Vietnam, that's all I can say. One day maybe I will.

The Fastest Boy on Wheels

Matthew Gopsill with Rose Impey

At the moment, the two most important things in my life are football and football – watching it and playing it. Who do I support? Manchester United, of course, who else? And my position's centre forward. I play for the school football team. They chose me because I'm great at heading. I used to be in defence but one day I scored a brilliant own goal. Everyone's still talking about it. We've got twenty matches to play this term. Last year we were top. Eas-y!

My name, by the way, is Matt Gopsill and I'm fourteen and a half. I live with my mum and dad and my brother Bash (more of that later).

Everyone says he's my brother but I have this theory he was left on the doorstep by aliens thirteen years ago. They still haven't come back for him, but who can blame them?

I'm disabled, but I'm not daft, although some people think I am. I can't walk and I can't use my arms, but I can work a computer and my wheelchair with head-switches. I can't talk either, so my computer has a voice box which talks for me – in a robotic American accent, I'm afraid. But none of this stops me from playing football.

Most of my friends are in wheelchairs like me, some can walk a little, but we make a wicked team. Our hockey's not bad either. Being in wheelchairs doesn't stop us, in fact, it's probably a tougher game, because legs can get trapped in the wheels. Also, there's the danger of low-flying hockey balls. They've made the hall at school a no-go area during break-times since Mr M. got hit on the head with a hockey ball. It was a good shot of Keeley's though. Not so good for Mr M.

Of course, having Conker helps me a lot.

Conker's my wheelchair, my jalopy, as Dad calls it. I call it Conker because that was the name of the horse who gave it to me. You think that's weird? OK, let me explain. My family and I were visiting a shop where my dad buys fish – exotic ornamental fish, it's his hobby. I was bored so I was playing football in the courtyard outside. This lady came out and was clearly impressed by how clever I was at manoeuvering my chair, but Mum told her it was wearing out and we were saving up for a new one. So this lady said that each year she organised a gymkhana to raise money for charity and this year she'd like to put it towards my wheelchair fund. My mum nearly snatched her hand off. We thought I might get maybe a hundred pounds, if I was lucky. She rang up a couple of weeks later to say she'd raised a thousand pounds. Wow! I couldn't believe it. A month later, she rang back to say it was now up to two thousand five hundred pounds and there was still more to come. In the end she'd raised three thousand eight hundred pounds. Whoopee!

I chose the biggest, reddest, meanest wheelchair I could find. It had to be purpose built for me because I use head-switches to control it. The electronic controls are made by the makers of Tornado aeroplanes and they'd never been used on this sort of chair before. Clever stuff, eh? Anyway, back to Conker. When they presented me with the cheque, the lady's horse gave it to me and, at the same time, they delivered my chair. Unbelievable. Now I really was the Fastest Boy on Wheels.

No one at school can keep up with me. On Sports Day, I was so far ahead of the others in my race that I did a U-turn and crossed the winning line backwards, to the cheers of my whole team. I can't help being a bit of a show-off.

Having Conker makes me pretty popular in the street too. Everyone cheers when I come out to play football with them. 'Be on our team, Matt,' they shout.

One of the reasons is they like to ride on the back, especially when someone's scored a goal –

we go round and round in circles. I wasn't quite so popular the time I rode backwards over someone's foot. I tried to tell them it was a tackle, but you should have heard the language. Good job my mum didn't. I'd definitely have got a yellow card.

When I go out in Conker I often have adventures, like the other week when we all went for a walk in Bradgate Park, which is near Leicester, where I live. I was powering away down this slope when a little old lady leaped out in front of me. She thought I was out of control and needed saving. I had to swerve to miss her. The expression on her face was brilliant and I had to laugh. Fortunately, so did she. That kind of thing often happens to me. One time a man was so busy staring at me he walked straight into a lamppost. I really laughed that time.

Some people, old ladies mostly, talk to me as if I'm a pet dog and pat me on the head. Or they shout at me as if I'm deaf. Last week, I went to Kwik-Save with my mum and Bash. Oh, yes, I was going to tell you where that name comes from. Well, he's called Adam, really, but he was in this play at school playing a character called Big Bad Ben the Belly-Basher. Great name, isn't it? And it suits him. So, Bash pushed me through this plastic curtain that you have to go through to get into the store, and this old lady came and pulled it aside and told Bash off.

'Be careful,' she said, 'we don't want to hurt his sweet little face, do we.'

P-lease. If I could talk I'd have told her, 'I'm fourteen, not four, you know!'

I just like doing ordinary things that other people do, like when we went away on our school field trip and we did abseiling, rock climbing, sailing and, best of all, riding on Death Slide. That was fantastic. They strapped me to a plank of wood on the end of a long rope and then pushed me off the top of a huge tower. A bit like bungee jumping, I suppose.

At the centre where we stayed, there was this long high ramp to get into the building and we had some brilliant races down it, full pelt, no brakes. Look out down below! Adults beware!

Fastest Boy on Wheels coming through!

And, best of all, I like doing things that people think I won't be able to do. Recently, we visited a mill and there were two ways to get to it: a road and a woodland path. They told me they'd never had anyone manage the path in a wheelchair, which always makes me want to do it more. I think, 'I don't care that nobody else has done it, *I can.*' So I did, and I told my mum to write in the visitors' book: *Matthew did it!*

People think I'm trying to be brave but I just think I'm trying to be ordinary.

Sometimes it's difficult to be able to just go off on my own and feel free. That's why our holiday this year was so great. We stayed on a farm in Cornwall and I could just go where I wanted and spend time with the animals.

There were two ferrets, Tinker and Fluffy, which climbed all over my face. They had really sharp claws and smelled like the dump, but they were great. There were two white goats, James Bond and Snowflake, that climbed up on the windowsills at night. We knew that because there was goat poo on them in the mornings. I was the goatherder.

I had butting contests with James Bond, with his head pushing hard against my trainers. I can't do much with my arms but my feet are dead strong, as some people at school could tell you. I can't fight like other people with my fists, but I can't half kick hard. So I won easily, the goat submitted. But I could tell he liked me because, later on, he jumped in the car and tried to eat my wheelchair.

The farm dog was called Bruno and the cats were called Rhubarb and Fudge. One of them kept lying on my tummy. I tried to push it off (not easy when you can't use your arms), but it kept coming back. There were some chickens as well and some day-old chicks. I held them and they felt dead soft.

The farmer's wife told us there was only one animal we needed to watch out for, the horse, because it didn't like cars or bikes or *anything with wheels*, but it came straight over to me in my

wheelchair and put its head on my shoulder. Dead friendly.

Animals usually come to me. I think it's because I'm disabled; they know I'm not going to hurt them. One night when it was getting dark and my mum couldn't find me, she looked in the barn. It was really dark inside and she could only just see me sitting there foot-wrestling the goats, with the horse's head on my shoulder. It was magic.

Towards the end of the week, my dad took us surfing. Dad had to hold me on the board because I can't sit with my legs apart or hold on to anything, and Bash held the other end. But I rode a wave. I really rode a wave. It was brilliant. Of course, the next minute I fell off, went under the water and thought I was going to drown. Good job Mum wasn't around; she'd have had kittens. But I'll tell you, with my bright blue and yellow wetsuit, my shades and my baseball cap, I looked pretty cool.

Talking of cool, I've just had my ear pierced. Jonny, my best mate at school, bet me I wouldn't dare have it done. He ought to know better than say that to me. It didn't hurt as much as my mum said it would, but I think she was just trying to put me off. *She* definitely ought to know better. Bash offered to do it for me at half the price with my dad's drill, but I thought, thanks, I'll leave it to the experts.

I got this big lecture from my mum about how she had to wait till she was sixteen and could pay for it herself and how much it hurt etc., etc. I told her, 'Well, it *was* the Stone Age. Putting a bone through your earlobe must have been painful.'

But at last I persuaded her, and we went to get it done at half-term. It only took a couple of seconds and Jonny had to pay up. It makes me look even more handsome than ever, if that's possible.

This term I'm going to start staying one night a week at school, in 'resi'. It'll give me a rest from my mum and my mum a rest from me! All my friends'll be there: Jonny, Adam, Jonathan, Michael. We'll have a great time.

Fortunately, none of my girlfriends stay in resi, which is lucky. Even if I say so myself, when it comes to girls, I'm like a magnet. They can't leave me alone. But, God . . . a fella's only got so much he can give. Even when he is the Fastest Boy on Wheels.

Drawing a Picture

Ashveena Rihal with Elizabeth Laird

I was sitting on the floor beside Ashveena and we were both drawing with crayons.

'Look,' she said. 'You can do it. Come on. Draw it, draw it.'

Was she talking to herself, I wondered, or was she talking to me? She tried to draw a line but it wasn't easy to control the crayon. She gave up and scribbled furiously on the paper but, as I watched, the crayon lifted from the page and wandered over her hand, then up towards her face. Her mum had told her not to do that. I could see that she was tempted though. She made a mark on her cheek.

'Mustn't draw on your hands,' she said.

'Mustn't draw on your face.'

Now the pencil was down on the paper and she was scribbling again.

'That's it. Good girl.'

It was as if she was giving herself instructions. She dropped the pencil and picked up a cloth. She's got a favourite one with a soft side that she takes with her everywhere. She rubbed her hands with it. She'd rubbed them so much already they were a bit sore. She rubbed at her face, too. I was watching her, wondering why she liked her cloth so much.

'Rubbing and scrubbing. Rubbing and scrubbing,' she said.

'What are you doing, Ashveena?'

'Rubbing and scrubbing. Washing my face.'

She was touching and feeling the cloth. Her fingers were working, patting, stroking, shaking, scrunching, rubbing and scrubbing.

Her mother came into the room. She'd changed out of her jeans into a rose-coloured shalwar kameez.

'Are you ready, Ashveena? We're going now.'

They were going to the Sikh temple for the evening prayer time and I was invited too. Ashveena was ready, except for her shoes. She was wearing the black silk kameez with a panel of embroidery down the front which Bali had brought back for her from India. She took our hands and walked towards the door. It was a huge effort. Her legs couldn't straighten to take the strain so she walked with them bent. It had taken her ages to learn to do this. She was holding my hand and she smiled up at me, and I could see that she was proud of herself, but it was obviously a relief when she dropped to her knees and crawled the rest of the way to the front door.

At the temple, everyone was busy cooking, getting ready for the meal that was going to be served at the end of the service. Auntie was here, carrying big saucepans of food over to the tables.

'Hello, my darling. Are you going upstairs? I'll see you later then.'

'Upstairs. Up the stairs.'

We took off our shoes out of respect before we went up to the big prayer room. Ashveena was getting ready to do the stairs. She gripped my hand and her mum's hand fiercely as her feet felt for the next tread. Her face was full of triumph.

'Up we go,' she said.

The priest was sitting at the far end of the big prayer hall. He was singing in a rich, melodious voice.

'Walk, Ashveena! Don't crawl!' said her mum.

I watched Ashveena and her mother make their way down the long strip of crimson carpet and reach the end at last. Ashveena dropped down on to her knees, tired out. Her mum put some money into her hand. She was supposed to offer it as a gift, putting it down on the carpet where other coins and notes were lying already. But this was a bit confusing. Ashveena didn't seem sure about where to put the money, or whether she should put it down or pick it up. But she did it right in the end. Now she had to stand up again and walk across the pure white cloths laid over the whole huge room. It was hard, hard work. She crawled the last bit, to the wall. We all sat down together.

She looked tired and sleepy. A friend was here already, a woman in a white kameez, sitting cross-legged by the wall. Ashveena was happy to see her. She touched her face and hugged her, then leaned against her side. She was enjoying warm arms and a soft lap, and a dreamy smile came over her face.

'Keep me in your blessing, my God. Keep me in your arms and make me safe,' the priest was singing.

'There was no way,' Bali said to me, 'that my daughter was going to be taken into care.'

Amrita, Ashveena's big sister, came up to us. She stroked Ashveena and the bangles on her wrists clicked and glittered. Ashveena touched them, and Amrita took them off and gave them to her. Ashveena played with them.

What does she like about them? I wondered. Was it the way they sparkled, or was it the noise they made, or the cool feel of them in her hands?

She held them and put them together, one by one, then two by two, then she put them

down, picked them up, and started again.

The room was filling up with people. The priest was singing beautiful words from the Sikh scriptures.

> 'God is one.
> Real is his name.
> Prime Creator.'

Ashveena put her hands together and bowed her head. Her mum had taught her this prayer but she wouldn't say it out loud. Her voice was no more than a fragile intake of breath and I had to lean forward to hear.

'Sat sri akal.'

The big room was nearly full now. There were over a hundred people here, the turbaned men on one side, the women in their bright flowing clothes on the other. Ashveena looked up at the chandelier, momentarily mesmerised. Then she looked away and began to smile and rock backwards and forwards. The pace of the prayer changed. There were some musicians sitting beside the priest and one of them tapped out a faster rhythm on the small drum. Ashveena turned her head and clapped her hands.

'Sit with your legs forward, Ashveena,' said her mum. 'Your muscles will all tighten up if you sit like that.'

Ashveena let Bali move her legs but a moment later she moved them back again. Two little girls, Kiran and Teeny, walked past. Ashveena watched them and nodded her head, alert. She held her hand up against her nose. It was her sign for sadness.

'You're not sad, are you, Ashvecna?'

The girls settled in the far corner of the room. Ashveena looked at her mum pleadingly and Bali smiled and nodded. Ashveena took off and crawled at top speed across the white sheets, past the rows of praying women. I followed her. Kiran and Teeny had got a packet of felt-tip pens. They were drawing to stop themselves from getting bored during the long prayers. They gave Ashveena some.

'Look, Ash. Do it like me.'

Ashveena tried to draw a line but it was difficult to control the pen, so she started making dots instead. She was talking quietly to herself while she drew. Sometimes I thought she was saying her own words. Sometimes it was as if she was repeating what other people had said to her.

'Busy drawing,' she murmured. 'How on earth do you do that?'

The felt tip moved to the back of her left hand. A big, blue mark.

'Mustn't draw on your hand.'

Now it wandered up to her face and there was a long line down her cheek. I could see she was being naughty.

'Now what have I been doing?'

Bali came up.

'Oh, Ashveena, look at your face!'

'Cheeky monkey!' said Ashveena.

Teeny gave Ashveena a crayon instead of a felt-tip pen and she went back to the paper and drew a careful line and some careful dots.

'Drawing a picture,' she said, and she looked up triumphantly.

'Did you hear that?' said Bali. 'First time she's ever said "picture". Clever girl, Ashveena.'

The priest's voice had slowed again. The music of his singing rolled round the room, a long, lingering sound. Ashveena knew this prayer. She dropped the pencil and put her hands together. Bali put her own round them. They leaned towards each other, their foreheads nearly touching.

'Free of fear.'

Bali said the Punjabi words clearly but Ashveena's were no more than a whispered breath.

> 'Meditate.
> Before time and in the past, he was the truth.'

She'd been excited before, with Kiran and Teeny, but she was calm and quiet now.

'Pray for peace,' the priest sang.

'It's time to go down,' said Bali. 'She needs to move. Scrunched up like that, her muscles will all tighten up.'

The worshippers were standing now. I was holding one of Ashveena's hands and Bali was holding the other. I could feel how tightly she was clinging to me, and how heavily she had to pull on my arm. As she walked across the snow white sheets, the women parted to let her through. Some faces turned away. Some smiled.

The stairs were hard work but the wheelchair was waiting at the bottom and Ashveena climbed in with relief. She pushed on the wheel and wheeled herself into the dining hall. She saw her uncle. He was at a table with Amrita. She wheeled straight up to him.

'Ashveena!' he called out. 'What? You still here? They haven't managed to get rid of you then? Haven't managed to kill you off?'

She was so pleased to see him she was patting and patting her hands. It was her sign for happiness.

'She speaks four languages, would you believe it?' Uncle said to me. 'English, Punjabi, sign language and one of her own. Don't think anyone understands that one except me.'

He gently buffeted the side of her face. She was rolling her head, plucking at his turban and beard, pulling him down to kiss her cheek.

'I can't think why she loves him so much, the way he beats her up,' said Auntie, who had been serving out the meal to people as they came downstairs from the prayer hall.

'You don't love me at all,' said Uncle to Ashveena. 'Bite me. Go on. Bite me.' He put his hand to her mouth. Ashveena laughed and kissed him again. Bali brought trays of food for us all, chapattis and dahl and sweet rice. Ashveena ate with pleasure, but I could see that it was hard for her to manage the spoon. A little yoghurt spilled down her black kameez.

'Hang on!' said her mum. 'Wait! Let me mop it up!'

Ashveena waited and tried again. I could see she was being careful. Uncle rubbed her face and wiped her mouth, though she could easily do that herself. But she knew what was coming. He was going to play a trick on her and she was ready, smiling with delight. He scrunched up the paper napkin and ran it over her head, then hid it in his hand.

'It's stuck in your head now,' he said. 'Look, it's gone inside your head.'

'Take it out!' she said. 'Take it out!'

He pretended to take it out. She giggled, her eyes creased up with laughter.

'Funny,' she gasped. 'Funny. Funny.'

Her hand was creeping towards his pocket.

Uncle didn't see. She found his keys and pulled them out. Now she was hiding them in her hand.

'Keys are gone!' she crowed.

They laughed and gently banged each other's heads together.

People were beginning to go home now. Teeny walked past on her way out. She waved goodbye.

'OK, Ash. See you.'

Ashveena waved back to her friend. Uncle stood up too, buttoning up his blazer. Ashveena waved at him like a queen.

I cupped her face with my hands.

'You're beautiful,' I said.

'Absolutely fabulous,' she said. 'Absolutely fabulous!'

The Frog Who Didn't Want to Be a Prince

Roz Davison with Cally Poplak

It's today; I'll hear the result today.

It's two o'clock in the morning and panic has already set in. What if I don't win? It seems so long since I handed it in, ages. They probably hated it. I bet I don't even get a mention. Then I'll never prove myself like I want to, like I've always wanted to.

You see, I was born with cerebral palsy. I looked it up in a dictionary once, it means paralysis of the brain. Not the whole brain, just the cerebrum: the bit that controls posture, balance and speech. Because of this, my life has never been what you'd call average.

It's not as though I think about it constantly. There are better things to think about. I'd describe myself as a normal teenager, if normal is the right word. I like listening to music, reading, watching TV, the usual stuff. If you came to see me, you'd probably find me talking on the phone to a friend, gossiping about who's snogging who, or what I'm going to wear to a party.

You might find me studying for my exams. I don't like school, who does? But the work is easy enough and I'm one of those people who gets really good marks without trying and could excel if I could be bothered!

I don't have a boyfriend, but I might do one day if the right lad ever comes along. So, no, I don't think about it constantly, just sometimes, if there's something on my mind, when it's night and I can't sleep and there's no one to talk to but myself.

The result I mentioned isn't some miracle cure for my problem. I don't believe they exist. No, this is much more important, because it has to do with real life.

It is the result of the annual short story competition at school. It's been going for years but this is the first time I've entered.

I've always loved reading. Poor Linda, at the library, has been pestered by me since before I could even walk, when I used to have to crawl up to the side of the counter with the books I'd picked. I've always been interested in writing stories too. If a story I was reading didn't end the way I wanted it to, I'd just make up one of my own. Being disabled, reading was a good hobby, because it didn't involve anything I couldn't do.

When I was little, my disability didn't bother me much. I never really felt like I was missing out on anything. There were things that I physically couldn't do, which my sisters did, but I just accepted it. I never felt different because I knew I wasn't different inside.

In fact, when I was very young, I never saw myself as disabled – never saw myself as anything out of the ordinary. So it came as a bit of shock to realise that when people looked at me, the first thing they saw was my disability and not the person I was inside.

I'm not surprised the way I walk attracts attention. Even I think it's a mixturc between the waddle of a duck and the crawl of a crab. In fact, the first thing most people notice, including me, is the way a person walks. That isn't the bad part. People noticing can't be helped, what's really horrible is the way people stare and point. They look at you as if, supposing you came any closer, they might catch something from you.

It's as though, because I have a weird walk, I must be weird, and not 'normal' like them.

When I was diagnosed no one was really sure just how disabled I would be. They knew I would be bad physically, but as for mentally, who knew? So, it's as if from day one, I had to prove my ability. I spent about five years in a special school, but it didn't take them long to discover there was nothing wrong with my intelligence.

'She doesn't belong here,' they said, 'she should be integrated.'

Which was great for me. It meant that, finally, I could stop spending my days dropping different coloured shapes through holes in boxes and go to learn more important things. Best of all, it meant I would be going to the same school as all my friends who lived near me.

I found it very easy to fit in at primary school, mainly because very young kids are too busy learning about themselves to worry about the differences between people. Anyway, from day one, I was determined to prove that I was just the same as them and they accepted me. It was very comfortable, being surrounded by my own group of friends but suddenly, at eleven, I had to move on.

But this time my close friends weren't coming with me. They were off to other schools. And so I started secondary school with people I hardly knew.

It was time to prove myself all over again and this time it was much harder. The kids were older

and they'd had longer to form prejudices. Some gave me pitying looks. A few insisted on helping me, whether I needed it or not. Others, maybe because I made them feel uncomfortable, chose to avoid me completely.

I don't know why, but there's always been this assumption by most people that if you are physically disabled there has got to be something wrong with you mentally too. People, who no doubt mean well, talk to you like you're a five year old with a mental age of two and a half. They're quite shocked to discover that you actually do have some intelligence and that you don't like being talked down to. Back then, there were quite a few people at my school who said I should be sent back to the special school. Which was why I had to battle to prove my equality, and my right to receive an ordinary education, just like everyone else.

And that was why the competition was so important. Why every victory is special to me, because it's always against the odds, because everybody thinks I won't be able to do something, so they use my disability as an excuse. But I always want to prove I'm not different. I may look it and sound it, but inside I'm the same as everybody else.

I'm in assembly now, waiting to hear the result. I'm so nervous. My whole year is there and loads of teachers.

'Third prize goes to . . .'

It's not me. Well, I might just manage second.

'Second prize goes to . . .'

That's not me either. That's it then. Although I clap the prize-winners, inside me the disappointment is burning! Not even a mention!

'And the winner is . . .'

ME!

I've won. They all clap. Of course, they have to clap even longer while I go up to collect my prize. But I don't care! For once, I don't even care that everyone is staring at me, shuffling up to collect the prize, because I've done it!

On my own ground, with a level playing-field, I've beaten them all!

As I make my way back to my seat, though most of them are smiling and congratulating me, I notice a few, the ones who imagine I'm a walking cabbage, look totally baffled.

And there are just one or two sore losers. They're sneering; turning to their mates and saying, 'I bet they only gave the prize to her out of sympathy, because of the way she is.' But later, when everyone's read the entries, they stopped saying that sort of thing.

My story was about a frog who refused to be kissed by the princess and turned into a prince. For a start, though he liked the princess and wanted to stay friends, he knew he did not love her.

But, far more important even than that, he did not want to spend the rest of his life being stared at, the way all princes are. He actually enjoyed the quiet life, swimming around with his fishy friends, or just sunning himself on a lily pad. To him, a constant diet of flies seemed a small price to pay for his privacy and being allowed to be himself.

I'll never forget the great feeling I got that day. The elation lasted for ever, until one night when I couldn't sleep and, again, there was no one to talk to but myself.

I was thinking, I suppose there'll always be people who doubt me because of my disability. Let them! But, having won that competition, I know that all I have to do, to make things happen, is to keep believing in myself.

Of course, it's always going to be like climbing a ladder. Something else I don't find easy! But if I can get on to one rung, why not the next, and the rest? It's all a question of never accepting the limits others would like to impose on me but choosing my own goals. Like the frog in my story, I'll decide for myself.

I may be different, but that doesn't mean worse!

Dear Diary

Lucy Mason with Jacqueline Wilson

Dear Diary,
I bought you today while I was out shopping for clothes. You were a right bargain. Two pounds ninety-nine! I could've got a cheaper diary, but all the one pound ninety-nine ones were made out of leather and I DO NOT agree with people KILLING cows for their skin or their meat. I can't say I have never had a pair of leather shoes before (or still do) but I try not to . . .

I don't really know how to start this so I'll just tell you a bit about myself. My name is Lucy Mason. I don't like my name very much, but it will have to do until I'm eighteen and can change it to something nice like Annastasya or Atlanta. I like unusual names! I also have a middle name. It's *Rose*. I hate it so much. I hate all flowery names except Daisy, because I have a friend called Daisy and her name really suits her. She's really nice. I met her through another friend of mine named Molly Mac – she's really nice too.

I am twelve years old (nearly thirteen). I like being twelve most of the time, but you don't have much power when you're my age.

I wish I could vote.

I wish I could drive too. I think I would be a good driver because I drive an electric wheelchair.

I'd like to be able to decide whether I want to smoke or drink. (Not that I would. I don't believe in people filling themselves with gunk just to comfort themselves. I think people have got into this thing where they find it easier to drown their problems in legal drugs than to talk about things.)

Basically, I would like to be able to run my own life without having to pay any bills. (Oh well, I can dream.)

I can mostly wear the clothes I want. I like wearing stuff from Miss Selfridges and Tammy. I usually wear long skirts and tight tops because they're comfortable and look OK. Once, I had this pair of square shoes my friend gave me as a joke birthday pressie. They weren't very comfortable to wear but they were great for taking off and hitting boys!

I have a heart-shaped face and big brown eyes. My hair is in a bob. It's goldie brown and has blonde streaks at the front. I like wearing nail-varnish in black, silver, blue and sparkly pink, and sometimes a different colour on each finger.

Sometimes me and my friends, especially Ellie and Shaima, have sessions where we pamper ourselves. Sometimes we do each other's make-up. For some reason, I tend to look like a vampire drooling blood when Shaima's finished putting make-up on me! (I hope she doesn't read this.)[1]

I am very small.

I am small because of my disability. It's called ostiogenesis imperfecta! But I just call it brittle

[1] Note to Shaima's mum: we never wear make-up out. Well, Shaima doesn't, anyway!

bones. It's easier to say, and it sums it up pretty well. I kind of wish I was bigger, but people will have to like me for *not* being six foot six!

At school I use a red wheelchair with black upholstery. It's a manual chair which means I have to push it around. At home I have an electric chair. It's army green. I want to bring it to school but the lift's not big enough. Luckily, the school's got a grant to build a bigger lift for me and the two other disabled people that go to my school.

When you're in your wheelchair, people can be very patronising!

Once, I was in a café and a woman came up to me and patted me on the head. I dodged her hand and asked her what she thought she was doing.

'I'm not a dog!' I exclaimed.

The woman was taken aback. Not only was she surprised that I minded being patted on the head like some pitiful puppy, but she was surprised I could talk. She turned to her friend and whispered something along the lines of, 'The unfortunate little doll can talk.'

'Of course I can!' I yelled.

I knew I wasn't meant to hear, but I did. I gave her a dirty look, and then briskly wheeled away!

I hate it when people are patronising, as you can see from the way I reacted. Some people treat me as if I'm different from everyone else. I'm not. It's just that I can't walk. I still like and do most of the stuff other young people do, so next time you meet someone like me on the street, don't pat them on the head. Just talk to them normally.

Anyway, let's get on to a subject a little less demanding. Things I like and dislike.

I like music (it must be loud) especially soul, swing, and some pop music and I keep something on continuous play, unless my mum is playing Bob Dylan or Melanie. I hate sixties music!

I like most food unless it's got meat in it. I'm turning vegetarian after I found out what was in sausages, but don't worry, I won't tell you now. I don't want to put you off your dinner. I like going shopping with my friends, especially when the cash flow is high. I spend most of my time parading round clothes shops trying all the expensive clothes on, or sampling things in the Body Shop that I'm not meant to sample. But if

I'm with Anna or Shaima we spend our time in the music stores down Croydon High Street listening in the listening booths. One of my friends, whose name I won't mention, got a bit carried away and started singing very loud.

I like my friends, especially Shaima, Suzi, Ellie, Liz, Helen, Gemma, Vicki, Mel and Anna. They're my group of best friends. I've known Anna all my life. We're kind of like cousins. We do a lot of stuff together and we speak on the phone nearly every night.

My mum's an artist. She is small and has layered red-brown and grey hair. (The red is not her natural colour.) She wears red glasses and has freckles. She uses a yellowy-gold wheelchair. Sometimes, we get on really well and have a laugh but, at other times, we're always arguing. Sometimes, it's over major stuff, but mainly it's over stupid stuff, like whether black makes me look dead! We also argue over the telly remote and what we watch.

I like soaps, animal programmes (as long as there's not too much blood), some documentaries, mainly the ones about people, not politics, and I *love* sitcoms. I like watching films on TV, but I like seeing them at the cinema more, especially when I go with my friends. Other things I like include swimming. I can swim eight hundred metres and I'm considering an offer of being coached by professional disabled swimmers. I love doing things with my friends.

I am quite lucky. At my school we don't have to wear a proper school uniform – just a school sweatshirt, T-shirt or polo-shirt. This means all my clothes allowance can go on stylish stuff. I have just started year eight. My school is a big comprehensive secondary school called Elliott. It has roughly 1,300 students. I get there and back in a taxi that I don't have to pay for, thank God. When I first went to my secondary school, I didn't know anyone else, but I quickly made friends with a girl called Ellie and then with Suzi, Liz, Mel, Helen and Josie. I am now friends with most of my tutor group. My favourite subjects are English, Drama and PE. A lot of people said that I wouldn't be able to do PE ''cos you're disabled'. I get remarks like that quite a lot. But I *do* do PE. I do everything my class does, just modified. Some of the girls at my school do football. I can't do football as I'd get crushed, but I like football. I support Arsenal – THE BEST! Most of my class support Man U and everybody argues about whether Cantona or Wright is the best.

Once, I went to a football match with my school. It was England v Bulgaria and I was sitting near the stand where the England footballers sit. Five minutes before the end of the match, Gazza got subbed so, when the match ended, I went to speak to him. I gave him this banner that me and my friend Ellie had made. It said:

MR DAVIES MAY BE FATTER THAN YOU,
GAZZA, BUT HE CAN KICK A BALL BETTER!

On the other side it said:

JOKE!

Anyway, he thought it was funny and he gave me his football shorts! (I wonder if they'll be worth a lot of money in the future?)

Now, here comes a grim part to my little story, so if you don't like blood and broken bones, then look away . . .

Last summer I was in my mum's electric wheelchair. I was going quite fast down the main road when a boy I know ran up behind me and switched the power off. The chair stopped so suddenly that the whole thing went over, including me. Unfortunately, because I have brittle bones and the batteries fell on my legs, of course, lucky me ended up in hospital. I've been in hospital thirteen times, but that was the worst. I was in intensive care for three days because I had smashed my head on the concrete and they had to keep an eye on me. Then I spent a month in an ordinary children's ward. I had loads of broken bones, including my left femur, both my ankles in two places and my right arm. Oh yeah, I forgot, my collar bone. I also lost two teeth but, luckily, they were baby teeth and grew back.

When I was on the wards I looked like a scientific experiment because I had so much equipment attached to me. I even had a heart monitor in case I had internal bleeding but, luckily, I didn't. Most of the nurses on the children's ward were really nice. I don't remember the ones on intensive care because I was in such a daze. The food on the ward was terrible. I'm not surprised that afterwards the people on the ward had eating disorders. Nobody wants to eat black chips and green splodge day after day. One thing that is good about hospital is not having to do any school work and having a laugh with the other young people on the ward. I don't know where they got the idea that hospital was restful!

Three of the nasty things in hospital were: bed baths prompt at seven o'clock in the morning with freezing cold water and face cloths that feel like they are made of coconut matting. The second thing's the bed pan. I hate it! It's a mini toilet that you have to sit on in your bed and it's made of metal – mega yuck. The other thing I don't like about hospital are doctors that say, 'This won't hurt,' and you know it will.

Even though I had a bad time last summer I have done loads of good things this summer to make up! Like when I went to Paris with Shaima and we went to Euro Disney. It was fun as the rides were good, and I could go on most of the ones my friend went on except for Space Mountain. It looked horrible to me. Well, it looked scary but exciting. You get shot out of a cannon, then speed into darkness along a track that flings you round a load of loop-the-loops and 180-degree twists. Euro Disney is really good. Although half of you wants to believe, the other half feels slightly stupid, especially when you find yourself flinging your arms round Mickey Mouse.

Anyway, diary entry, I've got to sign off now. There's a book of algebra waiting for me. I'll write again soon.

Yours,

Lucy Mason

The authors

Davoren Hanna was born in Dublin in 1975. He wrote 'Freewheeling Champ' when he was twelve years old for his hero, the champion cyclist Stephen Roche, who was a Dubliner too. Davoren had cerebral palsy, and he couldn't talk, or make any voluntary movements. He later wrote that he had lived his first seven years 'wordlessly as an apparently retarded child'. But then his family worked out how to help him communicate by pointing to letters on a big alphabet keyboard. It was very slow and difficult, but almost immediately he began to write poetry, and his poems soon started to win awards.

The Friendship Tree: The life and poems of Davoren Hanna, by his father, Jack Hanna, was published by New Ireland Books in 1996.

Scott Thurlby

When I met Scott, I saw a pleasant-faced boy seated in a wheelchair, with large, bronzed legs. It was hot and he was wearing shorts and a T-shirt. He has soft, dark brown hair cropped very close, dark brown eyes, neat features, a smooth, clear olive skin, and a gold stud earring in one ear. I noticed at once how small and finely shaped his hands were.

I asked him to name three events which he would never forget, either because they had been so wonderful or so awful, or both. He said, 'Wembley, Twickenham and Spain.' I said, 'You've got the wrong scribe for the first two. I couldn't get my head round football or rugby, so it will have to be Spain.'

When he began to talk, I discovered to my joy that Scott has a strong sense of humour, a sharp eye for detail and an invigorating racy style. We concentrated on Spain, and Scott opened my eyes not only to Spain, but to the trials and dangers of life in a wheelchair, and enlarged my mind wonderfully. He was sensitive to other people's sensitivities, which I liked, though it sometimes interfered with my writing self. I would want to put something in, because it was funny or because it pinned a character down, but Scott would veto it, because 'it might hurt.'

We talked of other things in between and were amazed to find we'd both been frightened of meeting each other! And found that we both love reading, especially, as Scott said, when we're 'snugged down in bed.'

I would like to express my warmest thanks to Scott's mother, Mrs Harris, for her help and hospitality (and Hayley, it was nice to meet you, too) and to Mr Smith, Head Teacher of Heltwate School who introduced me to Scott and helpfully sat in with us at our first meeting at the school when we were both so nervous of each other.

June Counsel

Rebecca Atkinson

I met Rebecca through my son Ben. She was one of the crowd of friends he brought home sometimes. At some point he told me that she and her sister were deaf.

Ben is also partially deaf. Meeting Rebecca was so good for him because her deafness didn't seem to figure at all. But this is part of the problem: deafness is both invisible – so that other people are unaware of it – and at the same time very isolating. It is easy to imagine that you are the only one. Since then, Rebecca has told me how good it was for her to meet Ben.

How did this story get written? Well, during our first conversation Rebecca told me how horrible she was to her parents when their marriage broke up. 'Did you feel bad about that?' I asked. 'Oh no,' she joked, 'I like being horrible!'

I felt then that we were on to something.

The rest of it is pieced together from conversations, notes, some observations from Ben and an element of fiction added to bind the brew. My job was to give shape to the story and to catch Rebecca's voice.

Rebecca is determinedly unheroic. She isn't pleased to be told she is 'brave', 'wonderful', 'marvellous'. She feels that you are only brave if you have a choice, and she hasn't. And when people say to her, by way of a compliment, that they 'forget' she is deaf, she thinks that is their way of denying it. The only time that she can 'forget' is when other people take the trouble to remember. She feels that her disability is part and parcel of who she is, for which she needs acceptance rather than admiration. She doesn't want a halo. She might be expected to live up to it. In her view, her disability makes her no worse and no better than anyone else.

But her way of coping with it *is* a matter of choice and makes her a pleasure to know. She is sparky, wisely observant, and far from horrible!

She has also made me aware of the progress that has been made in a generation or so for disabled people. My own struggle with deafness was made that much harder by the discouragement I met at almost every turn, and sometimes the outright rejection. Where I felt ashamed and apologetic as a youngster, Rebecca is open and confident. She knows what help is available and, while she is aware of the barriers, she assumes that she will have the same opportunities as others, which is everyone's gain. She says she owes a lot to strong parental support.

But there is still much room for improvement; the world is a very deaf place; shouting doesn't help I know, but perhaps this story will.

Joyce Dunbar

Sang Bradby

Nobody knows exactly when Sang was born, let alone who his other parents might have been. There were several accounts of how he first came to be found. In one version, he was picked up off a pavement in Vietnam by a passing policeman who handed him into the nearest orphanage. In another variation, he simply appeared one day in the office of the orphanage having been dumped there by someone unknown. The only (nearly) certain thing is that the orphanage was called the 'Hoi Duc Anh', in Vietnam.

In the Hoi Duc Anh, there was apparently never enough food for all the abandoned babies and toddlers, so prolonged malnutrition may have been the cause of some of Sang's disabilities. On the other hand, he may have been born disabled.

After a while, Sang was moved to a children's home in Britain, where he stayed for the next few years, until someone decided that they'd arrange for him to be adopted. We were the family chosen.

These days, Sang is a slightly shambling, reasonably confident young man, gentle with smaller children, always thoughtful about other people's needs. He has grown aware of his own needs, rights, likes and dislikes too. He is firmly rooted into the fabric of this family and the extended family. If visitors ask him about himself, politely and briefly he will explain, in his indistinct way of speaking, about his origins. Then he'll say, 'Ask Mum the rest. She know.' For a long while he's been content that we, his parents and family, should be keepers of his past while he gets on with the present.

Sang knows that he's disabled. But he didn't consider that was a very interesting thing to talk about. He chose to put the emphasis of his story on adoption because he reckoned it might be useful for someone else in the same situation. He talked into a tape-recorder, with me asking him questions from time to time. It's still sometimes difficult to understand his speech if you don't already know what he's trying to say. So then I typed it out, and read it back to him several times so he could change things till he thought it sounded how he wanted.

Like many adoptive parents of profoundly hurt children, we were sometimes told by ignorant people how 'brave' we were. Yet surely, it is he, and others like him, who are brave. To enter an alien household filled with strangers when you don't even know who you are yourself, is to show great courage.

Our son Sang, of whom we are immensely proud, took a great risk when he decided, round about the age of thirteen or fourteen, to stop screaming and to try to settle to the life he'd got. His reward is that eventually he found himself. And mostly, as you can see from his story, he likes the person he has found.

Rachel Anderson

Matthew Gopsill

I first met Matthew when I went into his school, Ashfield School, to run a writer's group. There were about eight in the group, mainly from Matthew's class, and we met in the library every week after school for two terms, sometimes doing as much talking as writing.

I used to be a teacher so I've worked with lots of young people, but never young people with physical disabilities before. I tried to work from their own experiences, using the things they were interested in. I don't exactly know what I expected them to be heavily into, but I didn't expect it to be football and hockey. When they talked about sport they talked with real passion and enthusiasm, and whenever I visited the school there was always a group skidding across the hall floor in their wheelchairs or on crutches playing a fast game of hockey. I think this encouragement of sport throughout the school helps to explain how confident and lively they all are.

Towards the end it was difficult choosing just one from the group to work with on this project. Matthew's writing showed real promise, and we clearly shared a similar sense of humour, but choosing Matthew presented quite a challenge, because he was the only one in the group who couldn't speak.

Matthew has cerebral palsy, which means he cannot control movement. As a result, he can't form words, even though he can make some sounds, and he can't use his arms, or sit unaided or stand or walk, although, as he tells you in the story, he has a very strong kick.

He can also move his head and he operates his computer by means of a head-switch. This is connected to a voice box which allows him to talk but, as he says, it's a strange, mechanised voice and the process can be frustratingly slow for him. Having said that, it was amazing to learn what a difference computers have made to the lives of young people like Matthew.

In the beginning, we would have been unable to communicate without his computer but, later on, we met in his home where we worked on his story using his mum as an interpreter. At home, Matthew often finds it quicker to communicate by head spelling. He does a series of rapid head movements which his mum spells out into words which I could then write down. Meeting the whole family meant that I learned a lot more about Matthew's life, which was a great bonus for me.

For this book, though, my only aim was to help Matthew, as far as was possible, to tell his own story, in his own words, in his own style. The title is his. It appeared as an odd line in the first piece of writing he did for me and it described him perfectly, as I think you'll see from his story. I suspect the grass will never grow under Matthew's wheels.

Rose Impey

Ashveena Rihal

Ashveena was born prematurely twelve years ago in Kenya. For a long time, she had to have oxygen to help her breathe, but in Kenya, where she lived, the electricity supply wasn't always regular. Sometimes, the oxygen was cut off and sometimes it was pumped too strongly. This damaged her brain so badly that her chances of survival weren't very good.

But Ashveena did survive. She was a fighter and she battled her way into life. Bali, Ashveena's mum, is a fighter too. She wasn't going to give up. Ashveena grew into a beautiful toddler, but it was clear she was going to need a lot of help, which she couldn't get in Kenya. Then, Bali's uncle and auntie wrote to her and said, 'Bring Ashveena over here, where we can help you and she can get some better treatment.'

So Bali packed her bags, scooped up Amrita, her older daughter, and baby Ashveena, and came over to London. Her husband stayed in Kenya. He's got a new family now. Ashveena, Amrita and their mum had to manage on their own.

For years the doctors did tests on Ashveena, and they found out she had a very rare condition as well as cerebral palsy. This meant that she'd always need help with walking and talking and the everyday things of life.

When I first met Ashveena, I didn't know what to expect. I knew she didn't always want to talk, and I knew she had what the experts call the 'mental age' of a young child. But I hadn't expected her to be so beautiful, with her oval delicate face, her huge, long-lashed eyes and her strong, black hair swept back from her forehead. She didn't say, 'Hello,' but her face broke into a smile and she put her hand out.

Ashveena can't tell her own story, and she doesn't talk about her feelings either. Perhaps it's the frustration of not being able to express them that makes her often burst out into fits of terrible rage and crying, when she bangs her head on the floor and no one, not even her mum, can make her calm down.

'What's going on in this head, eh?' Bali says sometimes, tapping Ashveena's forehead lightly with her finger.

I wanted to understand Ashveena. I wanted to know what she was thinking and feeling and what it was like to be her, but I knew it wouldn't be easy. When Ashveena does talk she doesn't always say the things you'd expect. Sometimes she sounds like a small child, and sometimes she sounds quite grown up. She lets you know what she wants and if she likes you and if she's happy or sad by her signs and movements and the expression on her face. But I knew that if I wanted to find out what was going on inside her head, I'd have to work a little harder than I would with most people.

Elizabeth Laird

Roz Davison

Here are three things about Roz: *Cry, The Beloved Country* by Alan Paton is one of her all-time favourite books; one day she would like to live in a cottage deep in the Irish countryside; she loves Leonardo DiCaprio.

Here are three things about me: *Cry, The Beloved*

Country is one of my top books too (except Roz first read it when she was fifteen, whereas I struggled to appreciate it until I was twenty-five). One day I would like to have a remote cottage on the West Coast of Scotland (Roz and I have agreed to do cottage-swapping holidays when the time comes). And Leo? Well, we can't agree on everything!

That's another thing about Roz – she likes a good debate, and she is a voracious reader, both of which explain her chosen A levels: English, History and Theology. Somehow she manages to juggle her studies at St Mary's College, Wallasey, with numerous extra-curricular activities. She also tutors a child with learning difficulties *and* helps children at the local primary school with their reading. That's her average week.

Roz is bursting with humour, curiosity and get-up-and-go. She won't let the fact that she has cerebral palsy get in the way of her ambitions. Many of the universities she would like to apply to don't have facilities and access for disabled people, but this doesn't deter Roz from her plan to read English at a university away from home (like every teenager, Roz wants her freedom and some fun!). And you won't be surprised to know that Roz is far more interested in talking about books and swapping reading recommendations than her cerebral palsy.

When Roz tells me she is going to be a writer, I believe her. You've read her story – she already is. Ask why she wanted to be involved in *Me and My Electric* and she'll tell you, 'I want to be published!' And when she starts talking money, agents and new writing projects, I know I'm talking to a pro.

Cally Poplak

Lucy Mason

I knew I was going to like Lucy. She'd written to me because she liked reading my books (a plus point in itself!). I wrote back to her, she wrote to me, I wrote again. Then I was asked to contribute to this book about young people with disabilities. I knew Lucy used a wheelchair because she'd drawn me a picture of herself in it and coloured it in carefully with her felt-tips. I'd commented on its beautiful, bright blueness. Lucy wrote back that the wheelchair was really scarlet, but her red felt pen had run out.

I knew Lucy has to use her wheelchair to get around because she has brittle bones. I'd briefly met her mum, Micheline, at a conference and I'd bought a book containing an article Micheline had written about Lucy. It was a warm, funny description of Lucy when she was little. On her first visit to a nursery school she'd been bored by all the little-girly stuff and had crawled off to play football with the boys.

So I wrote to Lucy asking if she'd like to contribute to *this* book. Think of the fame, I wrote. Think of the money! Lucy thought. Lucy wrote back. She said, 'Yes yes yes!'

I was supposed to help Lucy write her story, but Lucy isn't the sort of girl who needs much help. I just asked a few questions and got her to write down her replies. This started to get a bit tedious so she suggested we meet to speed things up a bit.

This seemed a great idea – but I felt nervous the day I went over to Lucy's house. We got on splendidly as penpals. We'd chatted happily on the phone. But what if Lucy didn't like me face-to-face? What if she thought I was old/boring/stupid?

But I needn't have worried. Micheline opened the door to me and led me into their stylish living-room. Lucy was sitting on the sofa, looking so smiley and friendly, I couldn't feel shy. She's very small so I felt big and gawky standing up, but as soon as I sat down beside her we were just two friends. She liked my big flashy rings – I liked her beautifully decorated fingernails. We talked clothes and hairstyles and shopping and music.

I suddenly remembered we had an article to write and produced my folder. I showed Lucy the things she'd jotted down a few months before. 'Oh no, I don't like *that*!' she said. 'And I *can't* say that. And I wouldn't *ever* think that, not now.' So we swapped stuff and changed all the choices. I'm pretty certain if Lucy had her way she'd want to rewrite her entire story, because she's so super-cool and up-to-the-minute that she's changing all the time. But, though her hairstyles and her current passions might change, she's still the same Lucy underneath – and I feel so pleased and proud to be one of her friends.

Jacqueline Wilson